a
HONG KONG
ABC

featuring
CHRISTOPHER & THE CAT

Written and illustrated by Jacqui Taylor

for Christopher, Lauren and the cat

Printed in Hong Kong / Production by Printline

• Second Print Production 1995 •

ISBN-962-85011-1-9

A is for abacus, ants marching by,
An aeroplane high in the blue autumn sky.
Aroma of apple pie in the afternoon air,
Amah asleep in the old armchair.

B is for beach at Big Wave Bay,
Bucket and ball we bought there to play.
Beautiful birds, blue butterflies bright,
Beneath a banana palm
... What a delight!

C is for coucalls, some cicadas too,
That called to the cat and Christopher, who,
Crouched under a Cycad
with congee to consume,
Were listening in awe to the creatures that crooned.

D is for dragon, dragonfly,
Dragonboat goes dashing by.
Drum, drum, drum,
you hear the beat,
Dim sum, durian -
eat, eat, eat.

E is for every Eastern delight,
From old eggs to eels, that glow in the night.
Electrical goodies, extravagant eats,
Eat, eye or buy these extraordinary treats.

F is for festival, the fung shui is right,
For a fever of fireworks to fill up the night.
Feast under a fa pai on favourite food,
Fortune cookies and flowers to flavour the mood.

G is for Gurkha
In the gorgeous ginger grove.
Glimpse the gecko, a lurker
Where the green grass grows,
And grasshoppers are jumping
Right under your nose.

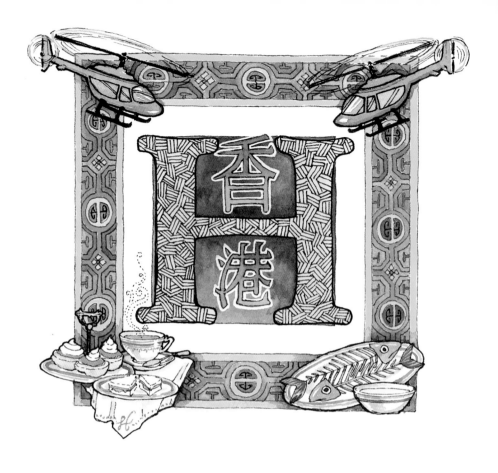

H is for Hong Kong - humidity, heat,
H is for high tea he ordered to eat.
Hakka hat hired to keep out the glare,
Hovercraft in the harbour, helicopter up there.

I is for idling on an imaginary island
With an indigo ocean and silver white sand.
Indulging in ice-cream and Indian tea,
Inhaling sweet incense 'neath the coconut tree.

J is for junk
On a jaunt past the Jumbo,
Just as a jumbo jets over Junk Bay.
Enjoying a jaffa juice, and jade-coloured jelly,
Jiving to jazz on the jukebox that plays.

K is for kumquat and Kung Hei Fat Choi,
Also for kites flown by two little boys.
Keeping them climbing requires a knack,
Climbing up high, o'er Kowloon and Kai Tak.

L is for Lantau, lychees for lunch,
L is for lotus, a lovely lush bunch.
Or a lively liondance with a laugh and a leap,
Leaving laisee for the lucky to keep.

M is for moon, Moon Cake Festival night,
Millions of lights make a magical sight.
Myriads of kites move like moths over the moon,
Munching a mooncake, it's over too soon.
Minibus, MTR... home before long,
Then sit yourself down
to a game of mah jong.

N is for nan yin man, narrator of note,
Came down from near Nan King on a small boat.
They nattered of ninety-seven and the noonday gun,
Noshed noodles noisily, naughty but fun.
Nathan Road's neon nightlife, not noticed at all,
Nor new fangled novelties on a barrow man's stall.

O is for opera, of Oriental creation,
Each actor a vision of outré ostentation.
Ornate and outlandish to fit the occasion,
Once the opera was over they received an ovation.

P is for pai yau, through it we passed,
Pavement game pai kau, learnt it at last.
Purchased some porcelain, pearls round and sleek,
Photographed a pagoda and popped up the Peak.

Q is for a quaint old sage queuing on the quay,
Quaffing a tinned ginger beer and staring out to sea.
Quian sticks for the temple, quail eggs for the pot,
A quid for the quinella... he quips he'll win the lot.

R is for rickshaw, that ran in a race
With a raspberry-pink Rolls-Royce
At a rip-roaring pace,
From a rendezvous point in Repulse Bay,
To the place where the races were runnning that day.

S is for sampan, alongside the Star Ferry,
Sampling spring rolls, star fruit and strawberries.
Across on Hong Kong side the skyscrapers soar,
'Shops selling suits and silks line the shore.
Statue Square Sundays - the place to be seen,
No. 6 bus to Stanley - the place to have been.

T is for taxi that gets stuck in a jam,
Then travel through town on a trundling tram.
Tai Chi Chu'an away from the throng,
Taking sweet tea from a street tai pai dong.
Typhoons to weddings, to almost anything,
Try just consulting the trusted tong sing.

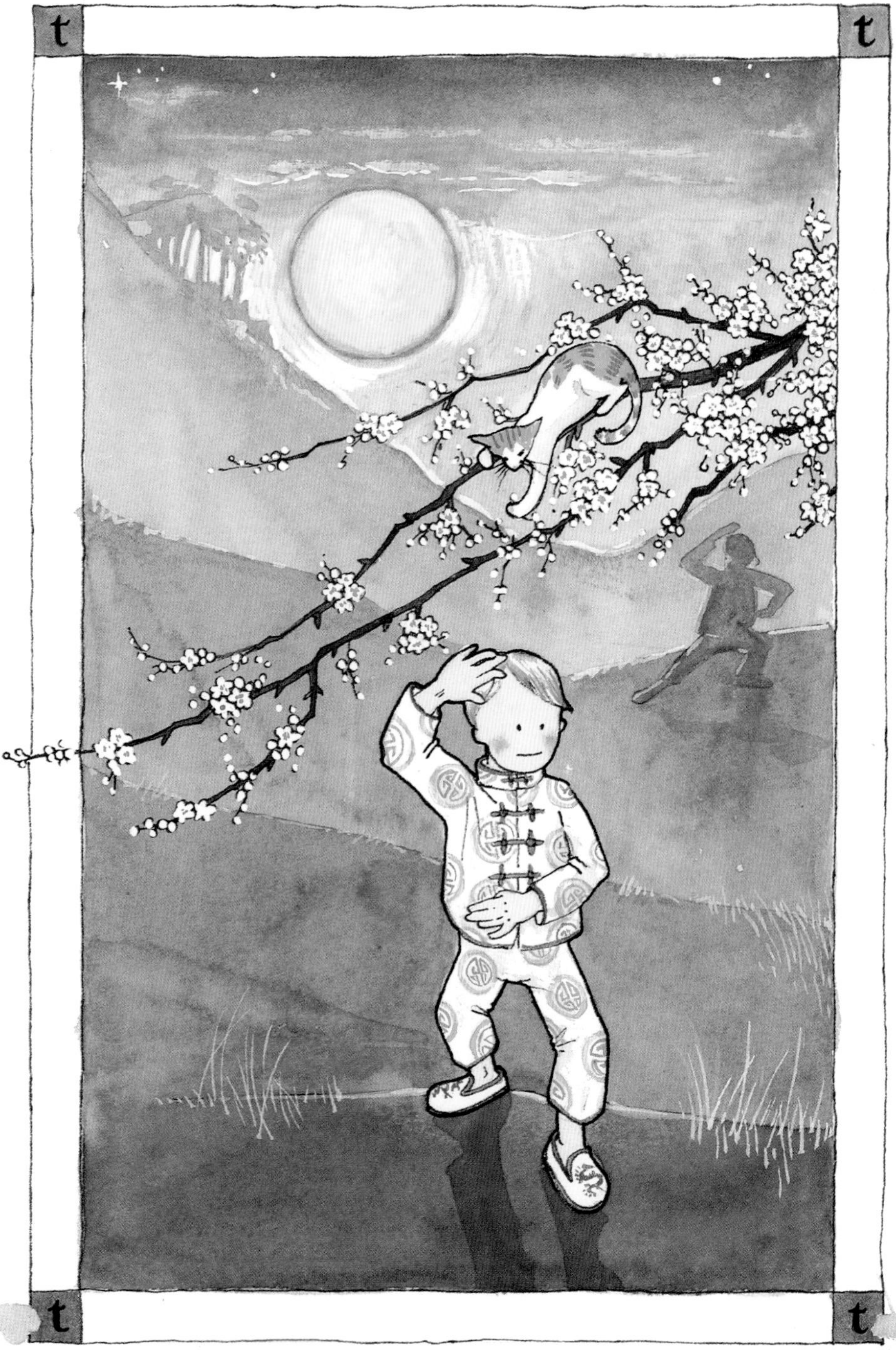
t
t
t
t

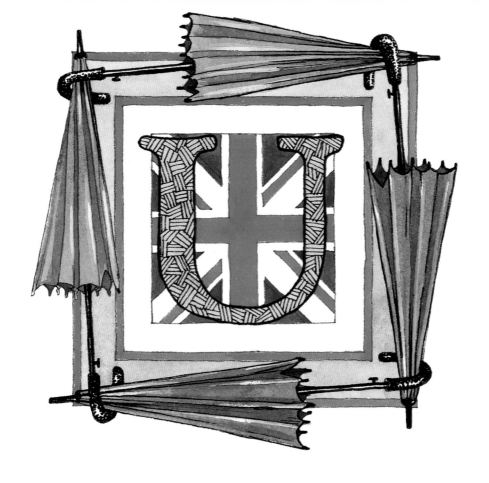

U is for the Union Jack upon his huge umbrella,
He strummed a ukelele to an unhappy looking fella.
Up above the underground
in the unceasing rain,
Others heard the cheerful sound
while dashing for the train.

V for Victoria ... her vanished days,
In Victoria Park her statue still stays.
Also for vege-man, in vrooms his van,
From the verandah they venture
To view what they can,
For value and variety, they vouch for this man.

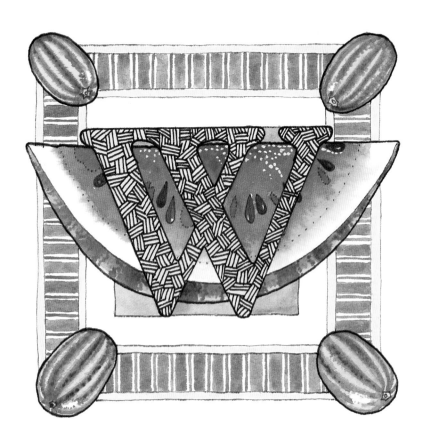

W is for walla walla that crossed the harbour wide,
Wallowing from Wanchai till it reached the otherside.
He walked to the walled city whilst whistling a tune,
Wishing for wet watermelon
in the wilting heat of noon.

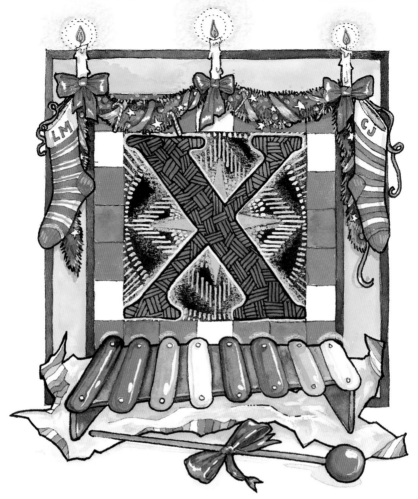

X is for Xmas - a parcel it brings,
Sent express from Yunnan in a place called Xuping.
From there to Xin'an and on to Ximeng,
From Ximeng to Xi'an and then to Xincheng.
When at last it arrived and its journey was through,
Inside was a xylophone shiny and new.

Y is for yin yang, yoga and youth,
Yoghurt and yum cha are tasty in truth.
Spinning a yo-yo keeps a good sense of fun,
Say yum sing, yum yum sing when each day is done.

Z is for zigzag and zippy and zoo,
For zucchini and zither and zodiac too.
A Zimbabwean story we'll bring next to you,
Of zebras and Zulus, giraffes and gnus.

Glossary

Aa

abacus
-a frame with wires, along which beads are slid for making calculations.

aroma
-a pleasant smell, usually of food.

amah
-a domestic helper. Originally all amahs were Chinese, now most of them are contract workers from the Philippines.

Bb

Big Wave Bay
-a popular beach at Shek O, on the east side of Hong Kong Island.

birds
-prized for their song and kept in beautiful cages, these birds are "walked", taken to tea and shown off by their owners.

Cc

cicada
-a winged insect that makes a shrill chirruping sound during the summer months.

coucall
-a fairly large, ungainly bird with a distinctive call. Sometimes called the rain-bird and commonly found in the outlying areas.

cycad
-a slow-growing, palm-like plant.

congee
-it is made from rice and resembles porridge. Usually eaten at breakfast time, garnished with chopped spring onions.

Dd

dragon
-a fierce mythical creature rooted in Chinese culture and tradition. Pictorial representations of the dragon are found in many places-on clothing, on money, in paintings, signs etc.

dragonfly
-a large insect with four transparent wings. Dragonflies abound in Hong Kong in the late summer and autumn months.

dragonboat
-each year on the 5th day of the 5th month is the Dragonboat Festival. Boats with dragon heads and tails race each other to the beat of drums. Large crowds watch at different venues throughout the territory.

dim sum
-Chinese snacks, served in bamboo steaming baskets, and consisting of morsels of meat or shrimp wrapped in dough and steamed or fried, buns and hot custard tarts. These are selected from a trolley that make rounds between tables.

durian
-a large and unusual looking fruit, very popular in Hong Kong. Banned on some public transport because of its smell, the saying goes "... tastes like heaven, but smells like hell".

Ee

eggs
-Hong Kong consumes 80,000 eggs a day. They come in many varieties - duck eggs, chicken eggs, quail eggs, salted eggs, pickled eggs and 1000 year-old eggs.

eel
-a snake-like fish considered a delicacy in Hong Kong.

electrical goodies	-Hong Kong is always a popular destination for the purchase of electrical goods and cameras at duty free prices.

Ff

festival	-of all the Hong Kong festivals, Chinese New Year is the most important. Houses and shops are decorated, debts are paid, houses are tidied and new clothes worn. Children receive lai see and most businesses are closed for several days.
fung shui	-is the influence of wind and water on a locality. Fung shui experts are called upon to determine the best position to place homes, gardens, roads and graves.
fireworks	-banned for the individual user in Hong Kong, but at Chinese New Year the territory stages a spectacular twenty-minute display above the harbour.
fa pai	-Large brightly coloured decorations made of flowers and crêpe paper and supported by a bamboo framework. The are hung over the entrance to a restaurant where a party or celebration is taking place.
fortune cookies	-novelty biscuits containing a slip of paper on which is printed some gem of wisdom.
flowers	-all homes are decorated with flowers at Chinese New Year. Many bought from the annual Victoria Park flower market. Peach blossom, plum blossom, narcissus and chrysanthemum are a few of the many on offer.

Gg

Gurkha	-Nepalese mercenary soldiers employed to patrol and police the border with China.
ginger	-found blooming abundantly in the New Territories in early summer. The roots of the ginger plant are often used in Chinese cooking.
gecko	-a small lizard with sticky pads on its toes. It is largely nocturnal and eats insects.

Hh

Hong Kong	-in the early days of Hong Kong the manufacture of incense was one of the few industries. The strong smell of incense gave rise to the name Heung Gong, meaning fragrant harbour, which then became Hong Kong.
humidity and heat	-for a large part of the year Hong Kong is very hot and humid. The humidity aggravates the already hot conditions and promotes the growth of mildew.
Hakka	-the Hakka tribe is an ethnic minority in Hong Kong. They wear traditional tribal head gear, a flat straw hat with a hole for the head and a black frill around the circular brim.
harbour	-Hong Kong harbour is one of the busiest natural harbours in the world, with ferries, hovercraft, lighters, pleasure craft, fishing boats and police launches all criss-crossing their way past each other.

Ii

incense	-is burnt inside temples, in front of ancestral shrines and at the entrance to homes. It is an important part of religious life here.

Jj

junk
-a Chinese fishing vessel made of wood, formerly all with sails, now most are motorised. Also junks are not used solely for fishing, some are devoted entirely to being pleasure craft owned by individuals, by companies, or for hire.

Jumbo Restaurant
-a large, beautifully decorated and brightly lit floating restaurant, several stories high, in the middle of Aberdeen Harbour. Most visitors to the territory like to see it, even if they don't eat there!

Junk Bay
-or Tseung Kwan O, is a huge housing development of tower blocks built on reclaimed land on Kowloon side.

jaffa juice
-juice extracted from jaffa oranges.

jade
-a semi-precious stone that comes in all shapes and colours from all over Asia. It is worn as a protection against disease and evil. It is a symbol of purity and beauty.

Kk

kumquat
-a small tree yielding orange-like fruit. Very popular at the time of Chinese New Year.

Kung Hei Fat Choi -Happy New Year!

kite
-the first silk kites were flown in China more than 3000 years ago. It is still a popular pastime among people visiting the country parks on a weekend.

Kowloon
-meaning nine dragons in Cantonese. Kowloon and the New Territories are part of the Chinese mainland and leased by Britain from China until 1997.

Kai Tak
-Hong Kong's only airport and one of the busiest in world. The approach to and landing at Kai Tak are quite spectacular. A new airport is being built on Lantau Island to accommodate the increase in traffic in and out of the territory.

Ll

Lantau
-a large island to the west of Hong Kong. It has a population of about 20,000 who live in developments and commute to work by ferry. Po Lin monastery is also found on the island and the world's largest statue of Buddha, cast in bronze.

lychee
-a sweet, white, juicy fruit with a rough brown skin.

lotus
-a type of waterlily with fragrant mauve flowers. Used in cooking are the plant's roots, leaves and seeds.

liondance
-it is performed by two people wearing a costume, one is the lion's head, the other the lion's rear. Most festivals or celebrations will involve a liondance, which is performed with great skill, to the accompaniment of drums and gongs.

lai see
-lucky money usually put into red and gold packets and given away at Chinese New Year. Children are the most common recipients, but unmarried people are sometimes given by married, and employees by bosses.

Mm

Moon Cake Festival — also known as the Mid-Autumn Festival. It commemorates an uprising against the Mongols in the 14th century. Cakes with messages hidden inside them were smuggled to compatriots, calling on them to revolt. To celebrate, lanterns are lit and processions held, moon cakes are eaten and the rise of the full moon witnessed.

myriad — a very vast number.

moon cake — a cake filled with a mixture of lotus or sesame seeds and dates, and sometimes a duck egg. Eaten around the time of the Moon Cake Festival.

minibus — a very popular, cheap way to travel around in Hong Kong.

MTR — stands for Mass Transit Railway. A very efficient, clean and cheap underground railway system serving Hong Kong and Kowloon.

mah jong — a Chinese game commonly played in Hong Kong, using 136 or 144 tiles or pieces. It is played by 4 people, the winner of each game receives payment from the other 3 players.

Nn

nan yin — a Cantonese form story-telling usually performed by two people. The first plays a zither and a clapper whilst singing the story and the second performer plays a two-string violin as accompaniment.

noonday gun — This gun is located in Causeway Bay opposite the Excelsior Hotel. It is owned by Jardine Matheson and Co Ltd. They have an employee whose sole task is to maintain the gun and fire it each day at noon. It is also fired at midnight on New Year's Eve.

noodles — a very common and popular Chinese dish.

Nathan Road — a favourite tourist spot for shopping, sometimes called the Golden Mile. Souvenirs, silk, cameras, watches and of course food, can all be found here.

Oo

opera — all Chinese opera uses elaborate costume, make-up, mime, acrobatics and swordplay. There are three different types of opera seen in Hong Kong - Peking, Swatow and Cantonese.

Oriental — of the East.

outré´ — a French word meaning unconventional or eccentric.

ostentation — showing off excessive wealth; over the top.

ovation — an enthusiastic reaction, usually applause, given for a good performance.

Pp

pai yau — a large ornamented gate leading through to a village or temple complex.

pai kau — Chinese dominoes commonly played on the pavement and involving gambling.

porcelain	-a wide variety of porcelain is available, from antique and rare, to very cheap. It is made into lampbases, ornaments, teaware and other crockery.
pearls	-all sizes and shapes, colour and quality are available in Hong Kong. For sale as individual stones or made up into necklaces, rings and earrings. Most good pearls come from Japan or Korea.
Peak	-a mountain behind Hong Kong's Central District. Many of the more exclusive homes are found on the Peak Road. A funicular railway, called the Peak Tram, transports tourists and commuters alike, up and down Victoria Peak.
pagoda	-a many tiered tower, usually a Buddhist temple.

Qq

queue	-a line of people waiting their turn for a service or item, (a common sight in Hong Kong).
quaff	-to drink in long drafts.
quian sticks	-these fortune sticks are shaken in a cylindrical container by the person wishing to have a question answered. When a stick jumps out, the number on the stick is read by the fortune teller and the answer is looked up in a special book.
quail eggs	-one of the most popular types of egg in Hong Kong.
quid	-one pound sterling.
quinella	-a special form of betting on the horseraces. Two horses are selected, and as long as those two horses come in either first or second, the punter wins his bet.

Rr

rickshaw	-from the Japanese word "jinrikisha", meaning man-powered wheeled vehicle, once a popular form of transport in Hong Kong.
Rolls-Royce	-Hong Kong has a great many of these stylish cars. Some privately owned and many for hire, or belonging to the smarter hotels as guest cars.
Repulse Bay	-on the South Side of Hong Kong island, it has one of the territories largest and most popular beaches. It is also quite a popular, albeit expensive, residential area.

Ss

sampan	-a small open boat used by a family to catch fish for a living. Also used to show tourists around such spots as Aberdeen Harbour or to ferry people to and from large boats within a marina.
Star Ferry	-a pleasant way to cross the harbour. The two-tiered, green and white ferries leave every seven minutes.
springroll	-a fried pancake filled with chopped vegetables.
star fruit	-a very pretty fruit sold in the markets.
silks and suits	-Hong Kong is as popular a place to purchase silks at a good price, as it is to acquire a custom-made suit or two.

Statue Square	-in the square is a statue of Sir Thomas Jackson, manager of the Hong Kong Shanghai Bank for twenty-six years at the turn of the century. It is a public garden, that on Sundays becomes the meeting point for the territory's thousands of Filipino Workers.
Stanley	-is a small market town on the South side of Hong Kong Island. Stanley's attractions include beaches and a market offering a diverse range of goods to the many tourists that visit.

Tt

taxi	-urban taxis are red with white or silver roofs. In the New Territories they are green and white. There are almost as many taxis in Hong Kong as there are private cars, or certainly it appears that way.
tram	-these run between the west and the east of the island on thirty kilometres of track.
tai chi chu'an	-is an ancient Chinese art designed to tone the muscles, using exercises that produce total balance and muscular control. It looks like dancing being done in slow motion on the spot. In the early morning you can see people practising tai chi in the parks or on their rooftops.
tai pai dong	-open food stalls operating on many of the smaller streets throughout the territory. Usually good value for money, although not operated under the most hygenic conditions.
typhoon	-these violent tropical hurricanes affect the territory between June and October each year. They leave in their wake damaged property, flooding and often injured people.
tong sing	-a Chinese almanac which many Chinese consult for the planning of their daily lives. It advises of festivals, seasons, solstices, equinoxes, horoscopes and so on. Also tells of good or bad days to marry, withdraw money from the bank, plant crops, travel, even to cut your hair. It also suggests talsimen as antidotes to unpleasant household spirits.

Uu

Union Jack	-the British flag.
ukelele	-a small four-stringed Hawaiian guitar.
underground	-(see MTR)

Vv

Victoria	-the first settlement of British arrivals in Hong Kong was named after Queen Victoria. Still named after her late majesty are, Victoria Park, Victoria Peak, Victoria Harbour and Victoria Barracks.
vege-man	-many residential complexes are visited by a travelling vegetable salesman in a van, commonly known as the vege-man.

Ww

walla walla	-a small motorised boat available for public hire, basically a form of water taxi.

Wanchai	-a business and entertainment area, between Causeway Bay and Admiralty, on Hong Kong Island.
Walled City	-a small portion of Kowloon was walled to keep an area nominally Chinese when it was given to the British. The Japanese used the stone blocks of the wall to build a runway during their occupation. So all that was left was a dense cluster of houses and shops interlaced with narrow alleyways. It has now been demolished.

Xx

Xuping	-a place in the province of Yunnan in mainland China. Xin'an, Ximeng, Xi'an and Xincheng are also all places in China.
xylophone	-a musical intrument, consisting of graduated wooden or metal bars, struck with a hard headed hammer to produce sound.

Yy

yin yang	-yin stands for darkness, femininity, passivity, wet things. Yang stands for light, masculinity, activity, dry things. The two words represent the nature of things. Chinese believe that harmony is achieved when yin and yang match with the five planets of Venus, Jupiter, Mercury, Mars and Saturn.
yoga	-a system of physical and breathing exercises, meditation and asceticism of Hindu origin.
yum cha	-this means "drink tea". Tea is taken with most meals by the Chinese and it is almost ritualistic.
yum sing	-this means "cheers" or " bottoms up".

Zz

zither	-a stringed instrument, placed horizontally and played with the fingers and a plectrum.
zodiac	-the Chinese zodiac is made up of twelve years, each year represented by an animal. The animals are the rat, ox, tiger, rabbit, dragon, snake, horse, sheep, monkey, rooster, dog and pig. The cycle is repeated every twelve years.
Zimbabwe	-a relatively small country, land-locked and to be found on the northern border of South Africa.
Zulu	-a member of the African Bantu tribe.